Name: _____

In the story you are going to read, a beautiful fairy tells her ugly
son that **if he lives with goodness and makes others happy,
he will no longer be ugly and alone.**

He doesn't understand what she means. What do **you** think
the fairy means?

D1231237

_____

_____

_____

_____

_____

_____

_____

The Black Heart of Indri

Dorothy Hoge

Name: _____

During your second reading of the story, you marked places where Indri and Nam Li show they have either a **good heart** or a **hard heart.**

Now look over your notes and write down at least one example for each character.

INDRI

GOOD HEART _____

_____

HARD HEART _____

_____

NAM LI

GOOD HEART _____

_____

HARD HEART _____

_____

Name: _____

Indri's mother tells him that if he lives for nine days and nights in the presence of **virtue,** his ugliness will vanish.

The word **virtue** means "goodness." It comes from a Latin word meaning "strength" or "power."

What power does Yua Nana's virtue have when she follows her father and offers her life?

_____

_____

_____

_____

What power does Yua Nana's virtue have when she laughs and plays with Indri?

_____

_____

_____

_____

Now answer this interpretive question:

Why can Indri be a good and happy person when he's with Yua Nana?

_____

_____

_____

_____

_____

_____

Name: _____

Near the end of the story, Indri says to Yua Nana,

> "How can I ever let you go? Without you I shall grow
> black-hearted again and shall surely die."

Imagine several weeks have passed. Indri and Yua Nana are
now settled in their house, and everyone has the water of life.
Indri wants to write a poem to tell Yua Nana how she
gives him life and why he needs her so much.

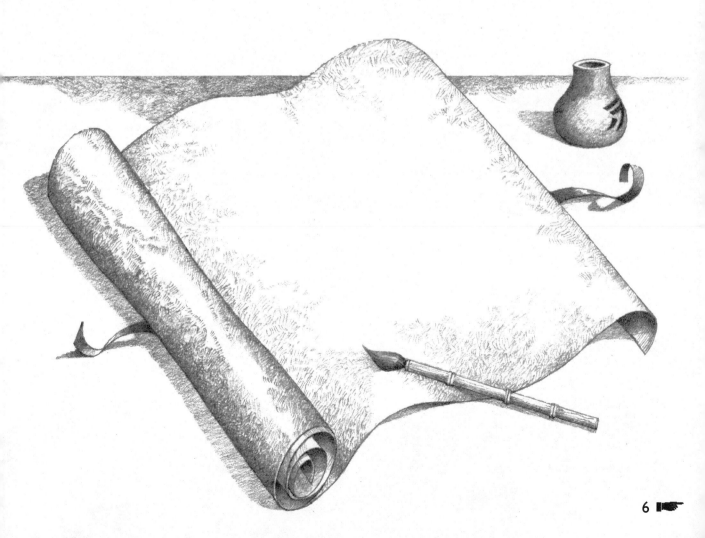

Poem to Yua Nana

When I was black-hearted,

I Kept the water of life for myself

I lived behind a thorny mimosa hedge

I _____

I _____

Now that I am happy with you,

I _____

I _____

I _____

I _____

Without you I shall grow black-hearted again
and shall surely die.

Name: _____

Like Indri, many of us need someone we care about to help us overcome unhappiness. Write an essay about a time when you were in a bad mood and someone brought you out of it.

Why were you feeling bad, and what was it like? Were you bored? Lonely? Angry? Sad? No fun to be around?

_____

_____

_____

_____

_____

_____

_____

_____

Who helped you feel better—a friend? A brother or sister? A pet?

_____

_____

_____

_____

What did your helper say or do to make you see things differently?

How did you feel afterward?

THE GREEN MAN

Gail E. Haley

Name: _____

A **cycle** is a pattern of events that occurs the same way over and over again. For example, the phases of the moon occur in a cycle.

What are some other cycles in nature?

_____

_____

_____

What are some human cycles?

_____

_____

_____

What makes you happy and sad about these different cycles?

Name: _____

During your second reading of the story, you marked places
where you **like** or **don't like** the way Claude is treating animals.
For each section of the story, choose one place and explain
why you like or don't like Claude's behavior.

Spring (pages 26-31)

_____

_____

_____

_____

Summer (pages 32-33)

_____

_____

_____

_____

Autumn (pages 33-35)

_____

_____

_____

_____

Winter (page 36)

_____

_____

_____

_____

Spring (pages 36-37)

_____

_____

_____

_____

Name:

In the beginning of the story, Claude is described as
arrogant, vain, and **selfish.**

arrogant

- thinking you're better or more important than other people
- snobbish, stuck-up

vain

- caring too much about how you look; conceited
- useless, idle
- foolish, empty-headed

selfish

- caring only for yourself
- not thinking about or sharing with others

Fill in your word in the blank space and find one or two examples
from the story that show Claude is being that kind of person.

Claude is being _____ **when he:**

[write your word here]

1. _____

_____

2. _____

_____

Name: _____

All of the people who have been Green Men and Green Women want to share their experiences about their year in the forest and their return home. Since they don't tell outsiders that they were Green Men or Women, they decide to start a newspaper just for themselves—
The Green News.

Imagine you were a Green Man or Woman and write an article for the newspaper. You can choose one of these topics or make up your own.

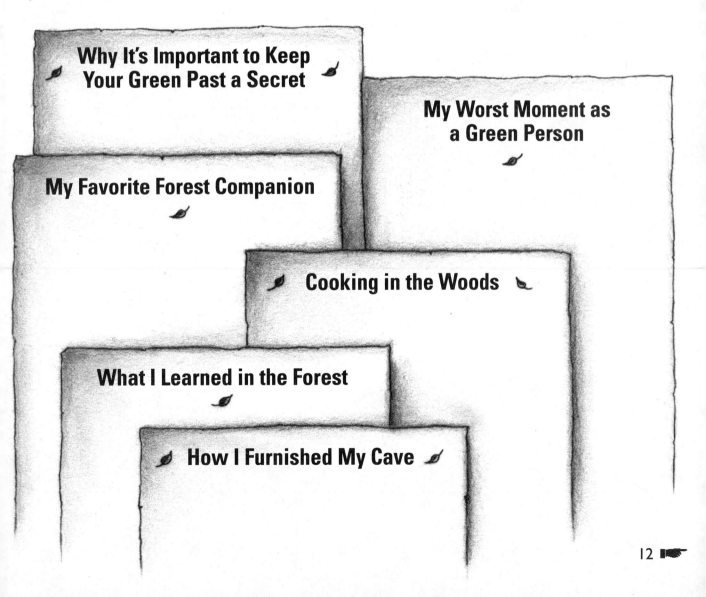

Why It's Important to Keep Your Green Past a Secret

My Worst Moment as a Green Person

My Favorite Forest Companion

Cooking in the Woods

What I Learned in the Forest

How I Furnished My Cave

The Green News

_____

_____

_____

_____

_____

_____

_____

_____

_____

_____

_____

Name: _____

When Claude was the Green Man, he learned to do things for himself. This helped him become a happier and more responsible person when he returned home.

Write an essay about something you learned to do on your own and how this made you feel more responsible.

What did you learn to do for yourself?

_____

_____

_____

_____

_____

Why was it important for you to learn how to do this?

_____

_____

_____

_____

_____

Did someone help you learn this, or did you teach yourself?

How did accomplishing this make you feel more responsible and grown-up?

THE MOUSEWIFE

Rumer Godden

Name: _____

At the end of the story, we are told that the mousewife "knows something" the other mice do not.

Choose two places you marked during your second reading of the story, and explain what the mousewife is **feeling** or **learning** that makes her different from other house mice.

1. What you marked: _____

_____ (page___)

Why you marked it: _____

_____

_____

2. What you marked: _____

_____ (page___)

Why you marked it: _____

_____

_____

Name: _____

The mousewife is inspired to free the dove because she feels **sympathy** for him.

> **sympathy**
>
> - feeling sorry or sad when something bad happens to someone else
> - having a lot in common with someone else; sharing needs, interests, or goals in a friendship
> - experiencing someone else's feelings as if they were your own

What **needs, interests,** or **goals** do the mousewife and the dove share?

1. _____

   _____

2. _____

   _____

When does the mousewife **experience the dove's feelings
as if they were her own**?

1. _____

_____

2. _____

_____

Now answer this interpretive question:
**How does having sympathy for the dove change
the mousewife's life?**

_____

_____

_____

_____

_____

_____

Name: _____

The mousewife is able to feel like a dove, although she thinks like a mouse. How would you describe in human terms what it would feel like to be these animals?

I imagine that a **tiger roaming through the jungle** must feel like I do when I

_____

_____

_____

_____

I imagine that an **eagle soaring through the skies** must feel like I do when I

_____

_____

_____

I imagine that a **crocodile lurking in the swamp**
must feel like I do when I

_____

_____

_____

_____

I imagine that a **dolphin romping in the sea**
must feel like I do when I

_____

_____

_____

_____

Name: _____

The mousewife and the dove become good friends, even though
they are different kinds of animals and each one is happy
to be the kind of animal it is.

Write an essay answering this question:
**Do you like your friends to be the same as you—
or different from you?**

What would
be good about
having a friend
who is a lot
like you?

_____

_____

_____

_____

_____

What
would be
good about
having a friend
who is very
different
from you?

_____

_____

_____

_____

_____

_____

_____

_____

_____

What kind of friend do you like the best? _____

_____

_____

_____

_____

_____

_____

_____

THE FIRE ON THE MOUNTAIN

Ethiopian folktale as told by
Harold Courlander and Wolf Leslau

Name: _____

Situation 1

Your best friend has moved away. It's Saturday
afternoon, the time when the two of you
used to get together, and you are really missing
him or her. Just then, the mail comes and you
receive a letter from your friend.

How would receiving the letter make you feel?

_____

_____

Situation 2

You have been hiking all day in the woods, but you stayed out longer
than you meant. By the time you start back, it's already getting dark.
You feel like you've been walking a long time, and you're getting
tired. Suddenly, the path turns and you see the light
from your friends' campfire off in the distance.

How would seeing the fire make you feel?

_____

_____

_____

How can a reminder of someone far away make us feel better?

Name: _____

During your second reading of the story, you marked places where Arha or Haptom **feels close** or **does not feel close** to other people.

Now answer this interpretive question:

Why is it easier for Arha to feel close to other people than it is for Haptom?

_____

_____

_____

_____

_____

_____

_____

Name: _____

Hailu's guest says, "Smelling is not eating, there is no **nourishment** in it!"

> **nourishment**
>
> ♣ what we need to live and grow

Everyone needs food, water, and warmth just to stay alive. But we need to be nourished by other things to live a full and happy life.

Check the things that Haptom has to nourish him at the beginning of the story. Check the things that Arha has to nourish him while he's on the mountain.

NOURISHMENT	HAPTOM AT THE BEGINNING	ARHA ON THE MOUNTAIN
Food		
Warmth		
Freedom		
Goals and dreams		
Close friend		
Sense of fairness		
Hope		
Respect for others		
Courage		

Name: _____

Arha survives the ordeal on the mountain because of his courage
and strength. But he also needs the advice and encouragement of
the wise old man.

Write a story about a girl or boy who is able to do something difficult
by receiving encouragement from somebody else.

How would
you describe this
boy or girl?

_____

_____

_____

_____

What
must he
or she do?
Why?

_____

_____

_____

_____

_____

Who gives the encouragement?

_____

_____

_____

_____

_____

How does the difficult thing get done?

_____

_____

_____

_____

_____

_____

_____

_____

_____

_____

Name: _____

All of us, like Arha, have wanted something so badly that we felt like we would have done anything or endured any hardship in order to have it. Write an essay describing a time when this happened to you.

What did you want?

_____

_____

_____

_____

Why did you want it so badly?

_____

_____

_____

_____

_____

_____

What did you do in order to get it?

_____

_____

_____

_____

_____

_____

_____

_____

_____

Why did or didn't you get it?

_____

_____

_____

_____

_____

_____

_____

_____

WOMAN'S WIT

Howard Pyle

Name: _____

How would you answer the question
in this nursery rhyme?

As I was going to St. Ives,

I met a man with seven wives.

Each wife had seven sacks,

Each sack had seven cats,

Each cat had seven kits;

Kits, cats, sacks, and wives,

How many were going to St. Ives?

Your answer: _____

Name: _____

During your second reading of the story, you marked places where the Demon is either **showing** or **covering up** his evil.

Now look over your notes and answer this interpretive question:

Why does the Demon sometimes cover up his evil and sometimes show it off?

_____

_____

_____

_____

_____

_____

_____

Name: _____

How would you describe the little Tailor in each of these parts
of the story?

Before the Tailor finds the Demon (page 75)

_____

_____

_____

When the Tailor opens the seven boxes (pages 76-77)

_____

_____

When the Tailor becomes rich and successful (page 81)

_____

_____

_____

When the Tailor gets ready for his wedding (page 88)

_____

_____

After the Tailor is married (pages 92-93)

_____

_____

_____

Now answer this interpretive question:

Why can't the little Tailor conquer the Demon by himself?

_____

_____

_____

_____

_____

Name: _____

The princess has become famous for her wit, and so she has started an advice column for kings and queens. How would she answer this letter?

Dear Princess,

A powerful Demon challenged me to a wrestling match last week. He said the winner would be the master over the loser *for all time*!! I am puzzled about what to do. Should I risk my kingdom and fight him? If I win, should I accept his offer to be my slave? (There are many improvements I would like to make in my kingdom.) Don't you think it's important for this Demon to respect me? Please answer soon.

Sincerely,

Desperate King

Here is a photo of the Demon.

Ask the Princess

Dear Desperate King,
My advice to you is

1. _____

_____

_____

2. _____

_____

_____

3. _____

_____

_____

Sincerely,

The Princess

Name: _____

The Demon, who is called an "enemy of mankind," has some very evil qualities. These qualities help make him powerful, but they also lead to his defeat. Some of these qualities are:

anger   cruelty   pride   greed for power

Choose the quality you think is the most evil and write an essay explaining why it is so dangerous.

_____ : **The Most Evil Quality**

Why do you think this is the most evil quality?

_____

_____

_____

_____

_____

_____

What does having this quality make people do?

_____

_____

_____

How
does having
this evil
quality lead
to the Demon's
defeat?

THE MAN WHOSE TRADE WAS TRICKS

Georgian folktale as told by
George and Helen Papashvily

BENNETT

Name: _____

Some people like to have the reputation of being a trickster.

Why can playing tricks make you feel powerful?

_____

_____

When might it be useful or necessary to play a trick on someone?

_____

_____

Why is it risky to play tricks on people?

_____

_____

Would you want to be known as a trickster?

_____

_____

Name: _____

During your second reading of the story, you marked places where Shahkro shows a great talent and places where the king shows a great weakness.

Now look over your notes and answer this interpretive question:
Why doesn't Shahkro just play a simple trick on the stupid king?

_____

_____

_____

_____

_____

_____

_____

Name: _____

When the king asks Shahkro if he thinks he is the trickiest man in the kingdom, Shahkro answers, "Tricking is my **trade.**"

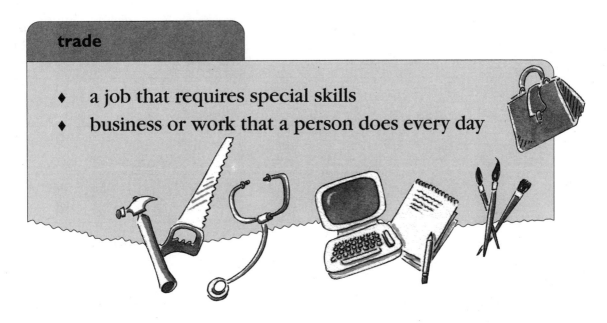

trade

◆ a job that requires special skills
◆ business or work that a person does every day

What **special skills** does Shahkro have that make him good at tricking?

1. _____

2. _____

Is Shahkro being modest or boastful when he suggests that tricking is **the work he does every day**?   **Modest**   **Boastful**

Why? _____

_____

_____

Now answer this interpretive question:

Why does Shahkro tell the king that tricking is his trade?

_____

_____

_____

_____

_____

Name: _____

Shahkro helps the people of his village by tricking the king. Write a story in which you play a trick, and everything turns out happily.

Whom do you need to trick?

_____

_____

_____

_____

What do you want to get from this person? Do you want to teach him or her a lesson?

_____

_____

_____

_____

_____

_____

_____

_____

How do you play your trick? What special talents do you use?

_____

_____

_____

_____

_____

_____

_____

_____

_____

_____

Why do things turn out happily in the end?

_____

_____

_____

_____

_____

_____

Name: _____

The quick-thinking Shahkro claims that tricking is his trade. Write an essay describing a talent you would like to be known for, and the trade in which you would use it.

If My Trade Were _____

What talent would you like to be known for?

_____

_____

_____

_____

_____

What trade would you pick to use this talent?

_____

_____

_____

_____

_____

What interesting things would you do if this were your trade?

How could you help others if this were your trade?

HOW THE
TORTOISE BECAME

Ted Hughes

Name: _____

What would be **pleasant** and what would be **unpleasant** about being:

The fastest creature in the world?

Pleasant: _____

_____

_____

Unpleasant: _____

_____

_____

The slowest creature in the world?

Pleasant: _____

_____

_____

Unpleasant: _____

_____

_____

A creature who lives with a big family and has lots of friends?

Pleasant: _____

_____

_____

Unpleasant: _____

_____

_____

A creature who lives alone and is the only one of its kind in the world?

Pleasant: _____

_____

_____

Unpleasant: _____

_____

_____

Name: _____

During your second reading of the story, you marked places where you felt **sorry** for Torto and places where you thought he was being **obnoxious.**

Now look over your notes and explain how you feel about Torto at the end of the story.

At the end of the story, I **do   do not**   feel sorry for Torto because

_____

_____

_____

_____

_____

_____

_____

Name: _____

Throughout the story, Torto takes **pride** in himself and in his ability to win races. Pride can be both good and bad. Pride is **good** when it gives you the confidence to like yourself and to use your abilities wisely. Pride is **bad** when it causes you to show off and to try to make others feel less important than you.

Is Torto feeling **good pride** or **bad pride** when he . . .

	Good Pride	Bad Pride
1. Tells the animals that they should respect him because he is a "genius runner" and was "made different."		
2. Strolls among the animals, happy and naked, not caring that the animals turn up their noses at him.		
3. Angrily rejects the idea of giving up races in order to have friends.		
4. Wants a special skin that he can put on and take off whenever he pleases.		
5. Thinks life is "perfect" because he has a special skin, can still win races, and doesn't worry about what the animals think of him.		

Name: _____

Part 1 **Create Your Character**

Imagine that you are going to create an animal using material you can find around the house. The kind of animal you'll make depends upon the weather outside and how the weather makes you feel.

1. What is the weather like on the day you make your animal?

_____

2. What is your animal's skin made of?

_____

3. What special things can your animal do because of its unusual skin?

_____

_____

4. What things would your animal find difficult or impossible to do?

_____

_____

Part 2 **Create Your Story**

Now write a story about how your animal wins the respect of other animals. Follow one of these two plans:

Your animal wins the respect of other animals by taking advantage of its unusual skin.	**Your animal wins the respect of other animals by overcoming its weaknesses and doing something difficult or dangerous.**

_____

_____

_____

_____

_____

_____

_____

_____

_____

Name: _____

In the story, Torto wants to be the only animal without a permanent skin, but he also wants to be accepted by the other animals. Write an essay answering this question:

If everybody started wearing a new style of clothes or hair that you didn't like, what would you do? Why?

_____

_____

_____

_____

_____

_____

_____

_____

_____

_____

_____

_____

_____

_____

_____

_____

_____

_____

_____

_____

_____

_____

_____

_____

TOM-TIT-TOT

English folktale as told by
Flora Annie Steel

Name: _____

Some things are all right for little kids to do, but people act differently as they grow older. What would you tell the little children in these situations?

Michael eats the whole plateful of dessert cookies before dinner because he is really hungry.

"It would be more grown-up to _____

_____."

Kevin just sits down and cries every time he is confused.

"It would be more grown-up to _____

_____."

Morgan hopes her friend will forget about a big promise she made.

"It would be more grown-up to _____

_____."

Name: _____

During your second reading of the story, you marked places where
you **blame** or **don't blame** a character for what he or she does.

Now look over your notes and answer this interpretive question:
Why does the girl deserve to live happily ever after with the King?

_____

_____

_____

_____

_____

_____

_____

Name: _____

In the story, the mother, the King, the girl, and Tom-Tit-Tot all make bargains. A **bargain** is an agreement between people that settles what each will give and what each will gain.

The mother **agrees** to let the King marry her daughter. What do the mother and the King hope to **gain** by making this bargain?

The mother   **The King**

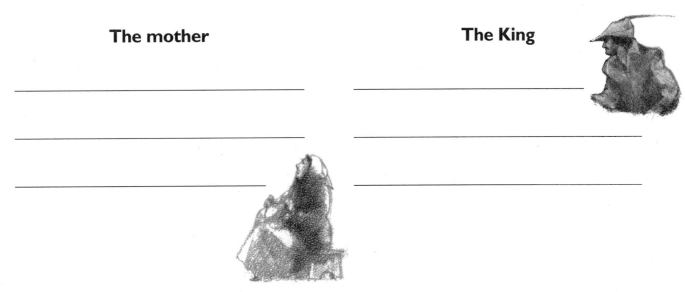

_____   _____

_____   _____

_____   _____

The girl **agrees** to let Tom-Tit-Tot spin the flax. What do the girl and Tom-Tit-Tot hope to **gain** by making this bargain?

The girl   **Tom-Tit-Tot**

_____   _____

_____   _____

_____   _____

Now answer these interpretive questions:

Is the bargain offered by the King fair? _____

Why or why not? _____

_____

_____

_____

Is the bargain offered by Tom-Tit-Tot fair? _____

Why or why not? _____

_____

_____

_____

_____

_____

Name: _____

Tom-Tit-Tot's scary spinning tail is a clue to his fantastic ability to spin skeins. Imagine your own creature who has an amazing feature and a secret skill to match.

Part I

1. What secret skill does your creature have? _____

_____

2. What special feature does it have that gives you a clue about this skill?

_____

_____

3. What funny or unusual clothes does it wear? _____

_____

4. What kind of mischief does it like to do? How does it use its skill
   to do this mischief?

_____

_____

5. What is your creature's name? _____

Part 2

Now write a boastful song that your creature sings when it uses its special skill.

Name me, name me not,

Who'll guess my name is _____

When humans look at me they see _____

_____

I look this way because I _____

_____

My idea of fun is _____

_____

Name me, name me not,

Who'll guess my name is _____

Name: _____

When the Queen finds out who Tom-Tit-Tot is, she is no longer afraid of him. Write an essay about a time when something seemed very frightening to you until you learned more about it.

What was the thing that seemed frightening?

_____

_____

_____

_____

How did you try to avoid it?

_____

_____

_____

_____

_____

_____

What did
you learn
that made this
thing no longer
scary?

_____

_____

_____

_____

_____

What
would you
do if you were
in a situation
like this
again?

_____

_____

_____

_____

_____

_____

_____

THE SNOWMAN

Hans Christian Andersen

Name: _____

Many times we like people who have qualities that are
very different from our own. To help you think about why
"opposites attract," imagine that the following things
are like people.

Why might a **cloud**
be attracted to a **mountain?**

Why might an **elephant**
be attracted to a **rabbit?**

Why might an **iceberg** be
attracted to hot, flowing **lava?**

Is there someone you like because he or she is opposite from
you in some way?

_____

_____

Name: _____

During your second reading of the story, you marked places where you **admired** the snowman and places where you thought the snowman was being **silly.**

Now look over your notes and answer this interpretive question:

Would the snowman have been better off if he had never known about the stove?

Be sure to give reasons for your answer.

_____

_____

_____

_____

_____

_____

_____

Name: _____

The watchdog believes he has **wisdom,** which he says comes from "age and knowledge." But even though he is old, he hasn't learned as much as he thinks. Let's look at these two passages from the story to see what knowledge the dog lacks.

The dog talks about when he was young:

···

"When I grew too big to lie in a lap they gave me to the housekeeper. She had a room in the cellar.—You can look right into her window from where you are standing.—Down there I was the master. It wasn't as nicely furnished as upstairs, but it was much more comfortable. I had my own pillow to lie on, and the housekeeper gave me just as good food and more of it. Besides, upstairs there were children and they are a plague, always picking you up, squeezing you, and hugging you, and carrying you about as if you had no legs of your own to walk on."

What doesn't the dog understand?

1. _____

_____

2. _____

_____

The dog explains

why he left the

stove:

"They threw me out, put a chain around my neck, and here I am. And all I had done was to bite the youngest of the children from upstairs. I was gnawing on a bone and he took it away. A bone for a bone, I thought, and bit him in the leg. But the master and the mistress put all the blame on me. And ever since then I have been chained."

What doesn't the dog understand?

1. _____

_____

2. _____

_____

How would you tell the dog he isn't really wise? What does he need besides "age and knowledge" to have wisdom?

_____

_____

_____

_____

Name: _____

I am _____

I am happiest when _____

_____

_____

_____

When this happens I _____

_____

_____

And I feel _____

_____

_____

_____

I am _____

I am happiest when _____

_____

_____

_____

When this happens I _____

_____

_____

And I feel _____

_____

_____

_____

Name: _____

The snowman's greatest and most earnest wish is to be with the stove. Of course, it is impossible, but that doesn't keep the snowman from wanting it anyway.

Write an essay about a time when you were little and you had an impossible wish.

What was your wish?

_____

_____

_____

_____

_____

_____

Why was your wish so important to you?

_____

_____

_____

_____

_____

Why was your wish impossible?

_____

_____

_____

_____

_____

_____

_____

_____

What made you finally decide that you could be happy even if your wish weren't granted?

_____

_____

_____

_____

_____

_____

_____

ELLEN'S LION

Crockett Johnson

Name: _____

Everyone, at one time or another, has mixed feelings about something. For example, you can feel excited about trying something new or hard, but still be afraid of it. When people have mixed feelings, they often figure out what they really want by **having a conversation in their heads.**

If you were both excited and scared about learning how to swim, you might have this conversation in your head:

The Scared Me:
The water looks so deep—maybe I'll learn to swim next year when I'm taller.

The Excited Me:
But the kids in the pool are having so much fun.

The Scared Me:
But what if I get water in my nose and mouth and they have to fish me out in front of everybody.

The Excited Me:
If Sandy can do it, so can I. Besides, I'll feel so grown-up when I've learned how to swim.

Now make up your own conversations.

Situation 1

I wake up in the middle of the night. **The Little-Kid Me** thinks there's something under the bed, while **The Grown-Up Me** knows there isn't.

Situation 2

A friend just told me that he or she is too busy to play with me right now. **The Angry Me** feels hurt, but **The Reasonable Me** knows that things aren't so bad.

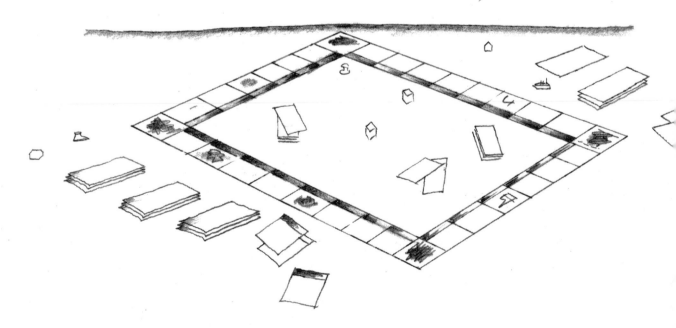

Name: _____

For each chapter, underline the places that tell you important things about **how Ellen is treating her lion.** Then write a word or two in the margin summing up how she is behaving toward him.

Conversation and Song

Here is how one person marked the beginning of "Conversation and Song."

Ellen sat on the footstool and looked down thoughtfully at the lion. He lay on his stomach on the floor at her feet.

"Whenever you and I have a conversation I do all the talking, don't I?" she said.

The lion remained silent.

"I never let you say a single word," Ellen said.

The lion did not say a word.

Kind; thinks about his feelings

"The trouble with me is I talk too much," Ellen continued. "I haven't been very polite, I guess. I apologize."

polite, friendly

"Oh, that's all right, Ellen," the lion said.

Ellen sprang to her feet and jumped up and down in delight.

"You talked!" she cried. "You said something!"

"It wasn't anything that important," said the lion. "And watch where you're jumping."

"It was the way you said it," said Ellen, sitting down again. "You have such a funny deep voice!"

Name: _____

Here are some things Ellen says to her lion in "A Kind of Silence."
What tone of voice does she use for each? How is she feeling when
she uses each tone?

1. "You don't have to exaggerate like that."

2. "Tell me now, honestly, aren't you ashamed of yourself?"

3. "I'm not paying the slightest attention to you."

4. "You've been sitting there all this time, seething with anger."

5. "And you see that you've really got to learn to control
your temper, don't you?"

6. "You made all that fuss over nothing at all."

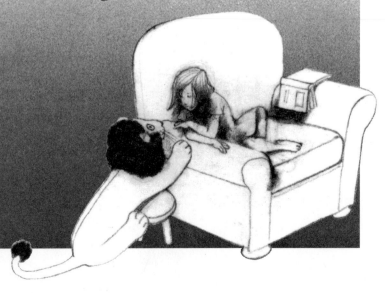

Now that you have thought about Ellen's feelings when she says
these things, answer this interpretive question:
Why does Ellen fight with her lion?

_____

_____

_____

_____

_____

_____

_____

_____

Name: _____

In "Two Pairs of Eyes," Ellen imagines that terribly scary things follow her in the dark. Write about a time when you used your imagination to frighten yourself on purpose.

Scary Fun

Where were you? Was it a new place, or a familiar place?

_____
_____
_____
_____
_____

What did you do to frighten yourself?

_____
_____
_____
_____
_____
_____

How did you keep yourself from getting too scared?

_____

_____

_____

_____

_____

_____

_____

_____

Why was it fun to scare yourself?

_____

_____

_____

_____

_____

_____

Name: _____

Ellen plays different games with her lion. She talks to him, looks to him for comfort and advice, and sometimes fights with him. How do you think Ellen would act if she were your friend?

Write an essay answering this question:
Do you think Ellen would make a good friend?

Mention three places in the story that help explain your opinion.

I think that Ellen **would   would not**   make a good friend because,

in the story, she _____

_____

_____

_____

_____

_____

_____

_____

_____

_____

_____

_____

_____

_____

_____

_____

_____

_____

_____

_____

THE RIVER BANK

Kenneth Grahame

Name: _____

What is Spring Fever?

_____

_____

How do you act differently when you have Spring Fever?

_____

_____

What wild ideas might you get when you have Spring Fever?

_____

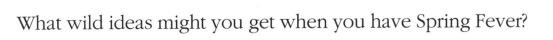

_____

Name: _____

During your second reading of the story, you marked places
where **Mole** and **Rat** show qualities you would want in a friend.

Now look over your notes and answer these questions,
giving examples from the story.

What do you like best about **Mole**?

_____

_____

_____

_____

What do you like best about **Rat**?

_____

_____

_____

_____

Name: _____

Mole loves the river the very first time he sees it. Let's look closely at this passage from the story to see why he is so fascinated by it.

•••

Never in his life had he seen a river before—this sleek, sinuous, full-bodied animal, chasing and chuckling, gripping things with a gurgle and leaving them with a laugh, to fling itself on fresh playmates that shook themselves free, and were caught and held again. All was a-shake and a-shiver—glints and gleams and sparkles, rustle and swirl, chatter and bubble. The Mole was bewitched, entranced, fascinated. By the side of the river he trotted as one trots, when very small, by the side of a man who holds one spellbound by exciting stories; and when tired at last, he sat on the bank, while the river still chattered on to him, a babbling procession of the best stories in the world, sent from the heart of the earth to be told at last to the insatiable sea.

What mood does the river seem to be in?

_____

_____

_____

What exciting stories could the river tell?

_____

_____

_____

Now answer this interpretive question:
Why is Mole so fascinated by the river?

_____

_____

_____

_____

_____

_____

Name: _____

At the end of the story, we are told that Mole "learnt to swim and
to row, and entered into the joy of running water; and with his ear to
the reed-stems he caught, at intervals, something of what the wind
went whispering so constantly among them."

On the other side of the page, write a poem about what Mole
hears the wind whispering to him.

The wind whispers in the willows.
It says to me:

" _____

_____

"You were _____

_____

_____

"Now you are _____

_____

_____

_____

_____ "

Name: _____

Mole's first day on the river is one of the happiest he has ever spent. Write about a day when you felt as happy as Mole.

What things happened on that day that made you feel so happy?

_____

_____

_____

_____

_____

_____

Was it a quiet and peaceful day, or a very exciting day?

_____

_____

_____

_____

_____

Were you with other people or by yourself?

_____

_____

_____

_____

_____

_____

How did your happiness make you feel emancipated?

_____

_____

_____

_____

_____

_____

_____

_____

_____

_____

THE OPEN ROAD

Kenneth Grahame

Name: _____

Which of these ways of life would you choose for yourself?
Circle the one you like the best.

Living in a snug, warm, and pretty
cabin, with a clean and sparkling river right
outside your door. You have plenty of time to
row in your boat, fish for your dinner, fix up
your cabin, and visit your friends
who live nearby.

Traveling around in a
circus cart equipped with all the
comforts of home, pulled by a friendly horse.
In the warm sunshine, you can go exploring
along backroads with one or two friends,
and maybe a pet, to keep
you company.

Driving a shiny new
sports car, speeding along highways
with no one to tell you what to do.
You can zoom through villages, towns,
and cities, and never run out
of places to go.

**Why did you choose this way of life? Why didn't you choose
the others?**

Name: _____

During your second reading of the story, you marked places where
Toad shows qualities you **would** or **would not** want in a friend.

Now look over your notes and answer these questions,
giving examples from the story.

What do you like **best** about Toad? _____

_____

_____

_____

What do you like **least** about Toad?

_____

_____

_____

_____

_____

Name: _____

Mole, Rat, and Toad are strolling along the road when . . .

•••

far behind them they heard a faint warning hum,
like the drone of a distant bee. Glancing back,
they saw a small cloud of dust, with a dark centre
of energy, advancing on them at incredible
speed, while from out the dust a faint "Poop-
poop!" wailed like an uneasy animal in pain.
Hardly regarding it, they turned to resume their
conversation, when in an instant (as it seemed)
the peaceful scene was changed, and with a blast
of wind and a whirl of sound that made them
jump for the nearest ditch, it was on them! The
"poop-poop" rang with a brazen shout in their
ears, they had a moment's glimpse of an interior
of glittering plate-glass and rich morocco, and the
magnificent motor-car, immense, breath-
snatching, passionate, with its pilot tense and
hugging his wheel, possessed all earth and air for
the fraction of a second, flung an enveloping
cloud of dust that blinded and enwrapped them
utterly, and then dwindled to a speck in the far
distance, changed back into a droning bee once
more.

What is "magnificent" about the motor-car?

_____

_____

_____

How is the "motor-car animal" different from the "river animal"?

_____

_____

_____

Now answer this interpretive question:

Why does Toad love the motor-car, while Rat and Mole are outraged by it?

_____

_____

_____

_____

_____

Name: _____

I loved _____

It was _____

_____

_____

It was _____

_____

_____

_____

_____

It felt _____

_____

Name: _____

You think your friend Toad needs some advice now that he has bought an expensive new motor-car. What would you tell him?

Do you think Toad should have left behind his canary-colored cart? Why or why not?

_____

_____

_____

_____

_____

_____

_____

Was it a good idea for Toad to buy the motor-car he wanted so badly? Why or why not?

_____

_____

_____

_____

_____

_____

_____

_____

_____

_____

What
would you say
to Toad as
he drives off?

_____

_____

_____

_____

_____

_____

_____

_____